A B C D E F G H I J K L M
N O P Q R S T U V W X Y Z

Meet big **G** and little **g**.

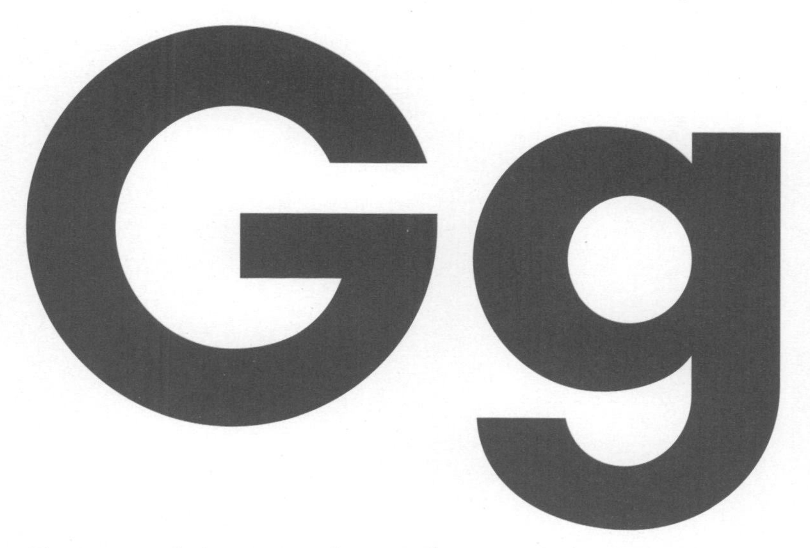

Trace each letter with your finger and say its name.

G is for

goat

G is also for

gift

garden

gorilla

guitar

Gg Story

Look at the **g**oat!
He's **g**ot a **g**ift.

The **g**oat **g**oes through a **g**olden **g**ate.

He **g**oes into a **g**orgeous **g**arden.

Then, he **g**oes up to a **g**orilla and **g**ives her the **g**ift!

The **g**ift is a new **g**uitar!
The **g**orilla is happy and so
is the **g**oat. Wiggle, **g**iggle!